Thru-the-Bible
COLORING
PAGES

FOR AGES 4-8

ILLUSTRATED BY JANET SKILES

™

STANDARD
PUBLISHING

Cincinnati, Ohio

THRU-THE-BIBLE
COLORING PAGES
FOR AGES 4-8

Standard Publishing, Cincinnati, Ohio
A division of Standex International Corporation

Scriptures are quoted from the
International Children's Bible, New Century Version, copyright ©1986,
1988 by Word Publishing, Dallas, Texas 75039.
Used by permission.

Cover design: Brian Fowler
Coloring pages: Janet Skiles
Project editor: Marcy Levering
Acquisitions editor: Ruth Frederick

06 05 04 03   9 8 7 6

ISBN 0-7847-0997-1

CONTENTS

Introduction 7
Bible Learning Activities
With Coloring Pages 8

SCRIPTURE   **TITLE** 11

Genesis 1   God Makes the World 11
God made everything! 12

Genesis 1   God Makes the Animals 13
God is great! He made the animals. 14

Genesis 1, 2   God Makes People 15
God made me special! 16

Genesis 6, 7   God Saves Noah 17
Thank you, God, for keeping your promise to Noah 18

Genesis 8, 9   God Gives a Rainbow 19
God, only you keep all your promises. 20

Genesis 12, 13   Abraham's New Home .21
God, you are awesome! .22

Genesis 13   Abraham and Lot 23
I can let others choose first. 24

Genesis 15, 17, 18, 21   The Birth of Isaac 25
What a special gift God gave Abraham and Sarah! 26

Genesis 24   Rebekah is Kind 27
I can be kind to others. .28

Genesis 26   Isaac Is a Peacemaker .29
I can please God by being a peacemaker. 30

Genesis 28-33   God Cares for Jacob 31
Yes, God keeps his promises! 32

Genesis 37, 39, 41   Joseph's Best Work 33
I try to do my best work. 34

Genesis 42-46   Joseph Forgives His Brothers 35
God wants me to forgive others. 36

Exodus 2   God Cares for Baby Moses 37
God cares for me. 38

Exodus 7-13   God's People in Egypt .39
Thank you, God, for helping me. 40

Exodus 14   God's People at the Red Sea 41
Only God could part the Red Sea. 42

Exodus 16, 17; Numbers 11   God's People in the Desert 43
Thank you, God, for food and water. 44

Exodus 19, 20   The Ten Commandments 45
Dear God, your rules are perfect. 46

Numbers 13, 14   Joshua and Caleb 47
I can choose right even when others choose wrong. 48

Deuteronomy 31, 34; Joshua 1   Joshua Obeys God 49
I can choose right even if I am afraid. 50

Joshua 5, 6   Joshua at Jericho 51
I can do what's right even when I don't understand. 52

Joshua 24   God's People Do Right 53
I can do right by obeying God's laws. 54

Judges 4   Deborah Helps Barak .55
I can help my friends do what's right. 56

Judges 6, 7   Gideon Is Brave 57
When I obey God, I am doing what's right. 58

Ruth 1, 2   Ruth Works Hard 59
When I work hard, I am doing what's right. 60

1 Samuel 1   Hannah Keeps a Promise 61
I can do right by keeping my promises. 62

SCRIPTURE **TITLE**

1 Samuel 2-4, 7   Samuel Does Right 63
I want to follow God. 64

1 Samuel 8-10   Samuel Anoints Saul 65
I will try to obey God even when I don't want to. 66

1 Samuel 15   Saul Disobeys God 67
Choosing wrong makes God sad. 68

1 Samuel 16   God Chooses David 69
I will try to do what's right even when I am afraid. 70

1 Samuel 16, 17   David Cares for His Sheep 71
God helps me do my jobs. 72

1 Samuel 17   David and Goliath 73
God helps me be brave. 74

1 Samuel 18-20   David and Jonathan 75
Thank you, God, for my friends. 76

1 Samuel 26   David Spares Saul's Life 77
God helps me be kind. 78

1 Kings 3, 4   Solomon Asks for Wisdom 79
God hears my prayers. 80

1 Kings 17   Elijah Is Fed by Ravens 81
God gives me food. 82

1 Kings 17   Elijah and the Widow 83
Only God knows everything we need. 84

1 Kings 18   Elijah and the Prophets of Baal 85
God, You are powerful. 86

1 Kings 22   Micaiah Tells the Truth 87
I can do what's right. I can tell the truth. 88

2 Kings 5   God Heals Naaman 89
Only God can heal people. 90

2 Kings 4   The Shunammite Woman's Son 91
God controls everything. 92

2 Kings 20   Hezekiah Is Healed 93
God hears my prayer when I am sick. 94

2 Kings 22, 23   Josiah and the Law 95
I want to hear and obey God's laws. 96

2 Chronicles 20   Jehoshaphat Prays 97
God hears my prayer when I am afraid. 98

2 Chronicles 33   Manasseh Prays for Forgiveness 99
God hears my prayer when I am sorry. 100

Esther 1-5, 8   Queen Esther Helps 101
I want to do what's right even when it is hard. 102

Nehemiah 2-8   Ezra and Nehemiah 103
I want to do what's right. 104

Job 1, 2, 42   Job Does Right 105
God will help me do what's right. 106

Daniel 1   Daniel and His Friends 107
I will take care of my body. 108

Daniel 3   The Fiery Furnace 109
I will worship God and put him first. .110

Daniel 6   Daniel Prays to God 111
I will pray to God every day. 112

Jonah 1, 3   Jonah Changes His Mind 113
I can do right by obeying God. 114

Luke 1   Zechariah and Elizabeth 115
Let's celebrate! 116

Luke 1   An Angel Visits Mary 117
Let's sing about Jesus' birth! 118

Luke 2   Jesus Is Born 119
Thank you, God, for Jesus. 120

Luke 2   Shepherds and Angels 121
We celebrate Jesus' birth at Christmas. 122

Matthew 2   Wise Men Worship Jesus 123
I want to honor Jesus. 124

SCRIPTURE   **TITLE**

Luke 2   Simeon and Anna Thank God 125
Thank you, God, for Jesus. 126
Luke 2   Jesus Obeys His Parents 127
I can obey my parents. 128
Matthew 3; Luke 2, John 1   John Baptizes Jesus 129
I want to follow Jesus. He is God's Son. 130
Matthew 4   Satan Tempts Jesus 131
I will follow Jesus when I am tempted to do wrong. 132
John 1   Jesus' First Followers 133
I will follow Jesus, God's Son. 134
John 3   Jesus and Nicodemus 135
I can be a friend to a leader. 136
John 4   Jesus and the Samaritan Woman 137
I can be a friend to someone no one likes. 138
John 4   Jesus Heals a Sick Boy 139
Jesus has power to heal people. 140
Mark 1, Luke 5   Jesus Chooses Four Followers 141
I can tell my friends about Jesus. 142
Mark 2   Jesus Heals a Paralyzed Man 143
I can be a friend to someone who is sick. 144
John 5   Jesus Heals a Man at a Pool 145
Jesus can do things no one else can do. 146
Mark 3   Jesus Heals a Man's Hand 147
Jesus can heal anything. 148
Luke 7   Jesus Heals a Soldier's Servant 149
Jesus is special. He can do miracles. 150
Luke 7   Jesus Raises a Young Man to Life .151
Let's praise Jesus! 152
Luke 7   Jesus Forgives a Woman 153
I can be a friend to someone who is sorry for doing wrong. 154
Mark 4   Jesus Stops a Storm 155
Jesus is powerful. He can change the weather! 156
Mark 5   Jairus's Daughter 157
Jesus can bring the dead to life. 158
John 6   Jesus Feeds 5,000 159
Jesus can feed a crowd with a little food. 160
John 6   Jesus Walks on Water 161
Jesus is more powerful than anything! 162
Mark 7   Jesus Heals a Deaf Man 163
Jesus is special. He can make the deaf hear. 164
Matthew 17   The Mount of Transfiguration 165
I will follow Jesus, our leader. 166
John 9   Jesus Heals a Blind Man 167
Jesus can make blind eyes see. 168
Luke 10   The Good Samaritan 169
I can follow Jesus by helping others. 170
Matthew 6, Luke 11   The Lord's Prayer 171
I can follow Jesus by praying to God. 172
Luke 12   The Greedy Farmer 173
I can follow Jesus by sharing. 174
Luke 10, John 11   Jesus Raises Lazarus 175
I can be a friend to someone who is sad. 176
Luke 17   The Ten Lepers 177
I can follow Jesus by being thankful. 178
Mark 10   Jesus and the Children 179
I can be a friend by being kind. 180
Luke 19   Jesus and Zacchaeus 181
I can be a friend to someone who needs a friend. 182
John 12   The Triumphal Entry 183
I want to sing praise to Jesus. 184
Luke 22   The Last Supper 185
Jesus wants followers to remember him in a special way. 186

SCRIPTURE	TITLE	
Matthew 27, 28; John 18-20	Jesus Is Alive	187
	"Jesus has power over everything!"	188
John 21	Jesus Helps Catch Fish	189
	"I know Jesus is alive."	190
Acts 2	Jesus' Church Begins	191
	The church tells everyone Jesus' good news.	192
Acts 3, 4	Peter Heals a Lame Man	193
	I can help sick people learn about Jesus.	194
Acts 4	The Church Prays	195
	I will pray for people who need to learn about Jesus.	196
Acts 8	Philip and the Ethiopian	197
	I can tell my friends about Jesus.	198
Acts 9, 22	Paul Begins to Tell About Jesus	199
	Paul learned that Jesus is God's Son.	200
Acts 9	Peter Raises Tabitha to Life	201
	I can show my friends that Jesus loves them.	202
Acts 16	Paul Tells a Jailer About Jesus	203
	I can tell others about Jesus even when it is hard.	204
Acts 21, 22	Paul Tells a Crowd About Jesus	205
	I can tell others about Jesus no matter what.	206
Acts 28	Paul in Rome	207
	Jesus loves everyone!	208

SCRIPTURE	VERSE	
Genesis 1:1	"In the beginning God created the sky and the earth . . ."	209
Deuteronomy 6:17, 18	"Be sure to obey the commands of the Lord your God . . ."	210
Joshua 24:15	"You must choose for yourselves today . . ."	211
Psalm 9:1, 2	"I will praise you, Lord, with all my heart . . ."	212
Psalm 86:9, 10	"Lord, all the nations you have made will come . . ."	213
Psalm 105:1, 2	"Give thanks to the Lord and pray to him . . ."	214
Psalm 106:3	"Happy are those people who are fair . . ."	215
Psalm 118:28, 29	"You are my God, and I will thank you . . ."	216
Psalm 141:3	"Lord, help me control my tongue . . ."	217
Psalm 145:21	"I will praise the Lord. Let everyone praise . . ."	218
Proverbs 4:24, 25	"Don't use your mouth to tell lies . . ."	219
Ecclesiastes 12:13, 14	"Honor God and obey his commands . . ."	220
Isaiah 38:7	"The Lord will do what he says . . ."	221
Mark 16:15, 20	"Jesus said to the followers, 'Go everywhere in the world' . . ."	222
Luke 1:30, 31	"The angel said to her, 'Don't be afraid, Mary . . ."	223
John 15:12, 14, 15	"This is my command: Love each other as I . . ."	224
John 20:30, 31	"Jesus did many other miracles before his followers . . ."	225
Acts 4:18-20	"So they called Peter and John in again . . ."	226
1 Corinthians 1:17	"Christ . . . gave me the work of preaching the Good News . . ."	227
1 Corinthians 11:1	"Follow the example of Christ . . ."	228
Ephesians 6:1	"Children, obey your parents the way the Lord wants . . ."	229
1 Thessalonians 2:2	"Before we came to you, we suffered in Philippi . . ."	230
1 Thessalonians 5:15	"Be sure that no one pays back wrong for wrong . . ."	231
2 Timothy 4:5	"Do the work of telling the Good News . . ."	232
1 Peter 2:21, 22	"Christ . . . gave you an example to follow . . ."	233
1 Peter 5:7	"Give all your worries to him, because he cares for you . . ."	234
1 John 4:15	"I believe that Jesus is the Son of God . . ."	235
2 John 9	"A person must continue to follow only the teaching of Christ . . ."	236
Index		237
Correlation to Standard's 4's & 5's and Primary Curriculum		240

INTRODUCTION

Thru-the-Bible Coloring Pages for Ages 4—8 includes Bible story pictures, application pictures, and memory verse pictures that correlate to the most popular Bible lessons for young children.

A Bible story coloring page provides a quick and easy way to introduce a Bible story or help children review the story. Most of the application coloring pages feature modern-day children and will help the learners take the Bible lesson home. The memory verse coloring pages use simple and shortened verses that the children can easily remember and use.

Children 4- to 8-years old are still developing their fine motor skills. They are experimenting with crayons and colors on paper as well as working toward a finished piece. Many young children are not capable of coloring within the lines or filling in every space on the page. Encourage children to keep exploring as you help them have fun coloring and learning about Bible things.

Guided conversation is important in making any activity a Bible-learning activity. Use conversation about the coloring page the child is working on to focus the child's thoughts on retelling the Bible story, naming ways to follow the example in the picture, or remembering helpful Bible words.

While a simple coloring activity is fun for many young children, consider making it part of a more active learning experience. The following pages suggest ways to use coloring pages in age-appropriate learning activities for your children.

BIBLE LEARNING ACTIVITIES
WITH COLORING PAGES

MORE THAN JUST CRAYONS

Four- to eight-year olds are capable of holding smaller crayons instead of the big ones. Most kindergarten and primary teachers encourage the children to work at staying in the lines while coloring. To vary the activities using this coloring book, you might want to incorporate some of the following ideas.

TOUCH AND FEEL PICTURES

Copy the coloring page and mount each child's page on poster board or tagboard. Provide one or more of the following items for children to glue to their pictures: rice, beans, cotton, glitter, fabric, felt, popped popcorn.

DRY RICE PICTURES

You will need 4 cups uncooked rice, food coloring (red, green, blue, yellow), plastic bags, wax paper, four bowls, poster board or tagboard, glue. Put five drops of food coloring in each bag. Add 1 cup of rice to each bag. Seal and shake the bag to coat the rice. Pour the dyed rice onto wax paper and allow it to dry. Put dried rice into bowls. Copy a coloring page for each child and mount each one on poster board or tagboard. Children glue the dyed rice to their coloring pages.

CLASSROOM BIG BOOK

Use a large piece of poster board for each page of the book. Allow children to choose what kind of a book to make or provide each child a coloring page based on your teaching theme. Give children time to color their pages, then mount one page on each piece of poster board. Ask each child to dictate a sentence or two for her page in the book. Print the child's dictation under her picture and let her finish the page with a border, stickers, or fun designs. Put the big book together with three large rings. Have fun reading the book together.

THEMATIC BULLETIN BOARD

Choose coloring pages based on a teaching theme. (See the index for Bible themes.) Let the children color the pages and add them to a bulletin board with an appropriate title. Consider cutting off the caption of the coloring page and allowing each child to dictate a sentence about his picture. Take pictures of your students and display each child's picture and name beside his coloring page. A bulletin board mounted low on the wall would be ideal for this activity.

BIBLE LESSON VISUAL

Choose a coloring page that illustrates a story or application you want to teach. Enlarge the picture and enlist the help of older children to color it appropriately. Mount it and cover it with clear self-adhesive paper. Use the picture to introduce or review a story, or use the picture to talk about the lesson application. It will be sturdy enough for young children to hold and pass around the story circle.

PERSONAL COLORING BOOKS

Choose coloring pages based on the theme you are teaching. Copy ten to fifteen different pages for each child. Make each child a personal coloring book: use staples, yarn, or folders to keep the pages together. Let the children take them home and encourage family coloring fun and Bible learning at home.

MEMORY VERSE POSTER

Choose an appropriate Bible verse coloring page and make a copy for each child. Let each child color the verse page and then mount the page on construction paper. Adding borders of popped popcorn, stickers, rickrack, or fingerprints make the posters fun! Encourage children (and parents) to hang the poster in the child's room or play area.

PUZZLES

Copy, color, and mount on tagboard a coloring page that correlates to your teaching theme. Depending on the age of your students, cut the page into puzzle pieces (4–6 pieces for the youngest, 10–12 pieces for older children). Keep the pieces in a large resealable bag with a uncut coloring page. Many children will enjoy placing the pieces on the uncut page; others will want to work the puzzle without the uncut page.

PLACE MATS

For special days and holidays, children can make place mats with coloring pages. Choose an appropriate picture to copy for each child. Pictures of creation work well for Thanksgiving, pictures of Jesus' birth certainly work for Christmas, and pictures of mothers or fathers with children work for Mother's Day and Father's Day. After children have colored their pages, mount each on a large sheet of construction paper, leaving room on one side for writing. Allow each child to dictate a sentence about the picture. Print the child's sentence on her construction paper. (Examples: We celebrate Christmas because Jesus was born. Thank you, God, for fruit. Thank you, God, for my mother.) Finish decorating the place mats, then cover them with clear self-adhesive paper.

PRAYER TIME

Choose coloring pages that correlate to your teaching theme, or choose coloring pages that show a variety of things that show God's care. Display the pages and use them to focus the children's thoughts for prayer time. You might say: "This picture shows something that God made. Thank you, God, for fruit. Ethan, what would you like thank God for this morning?" Or, "This picture shows a way that God cares for us. Megan, how does God care for you? Let's thank God right now."

ACT IT OUT

Choose coloring pages that illustrate ways to help others. Display one page on each wall of the room. Travel with your children to the first wall. Talk about the picture, then ask everyone to act it out with a friend. Continue traveling around the room and acting out each picture.

BEAN BAG GAME

Tape together four to eight coloring pages that correlate to stories the children have learned. Place the grouped pictures on the floor. Give each child a turn to throw a bean bag at one of the pages and tell something about that Bible story.

3-DIMENSIONAL PICTURE

Make two copies of a picture for each of your students. Let them color both pictures then cut out figures from one picture and glue them to the same spot on the uncut picture. Have them glue small folded pieces of paper in between to give them a 3-dimensional look. You can also make pop-up pictures by gluing one end of an accordion-folded strip of paper to the cut-out picture and the other end to the uncut picture.

MOSAIC PICTURE

Have students make a mosaic picture by having them glue small pieces of torn construction to the picture using corresponding colors.

MAIL IT HOME

For absentees or for a fun way to contact visitors, mail the coloring pages home with a note to the child. Children love to get mail, especially mail with a special activity to complete.

God Makes the World
Genesis 1

God made everything!

God Makes the Animals

Genesis 1

God is great! He made the animals.

God Makes People
Genesis 1, 2

God made me special!

God Saves Noah

Genesis 6, 7

Thank you, God, for keeping your promise to Noah.

God Gives a Rainbow

Genesis 8, 9

God, only you keep all your promises.

Abraham's New Home
Genesis 12, 13

God, you are awesome!

Abraham and Lot

Genesis 13

I can let others choose first.

The Birth of Isaac
Genesis 15, 17, 18, 21

What a special gift God gave Abraham and Sarah!

Rebekah is Kind

Genesis 24

I can be kind to others.

Isaac Is a Peacemaker
Genesis 26

I can please God by being a peacemaker.

God Cares for Jacob
Genesis 28-33

Yes, God keeps his promises!

Joseph's Best Work
Genesis 37, 39, 41

I try to do my best work.

Joseph Forgives His Brothers
Genesis 42-46

God wants me to forgive others.

God Cares for Baby Moses
Exodus 2

God cares for me.

God's People in Egypt
Exodus 7-13

Thank you, God, for helping me.

God's People at the Red Sea
Exodus 14

Only God could part the Red Sea.

God's People in the Desert
Exodus 16, 17; Numbers 11

Thank you, God, for food and water.

The Ten Commandments
Exodus 19, 20

Dear God, your rules are perfect.

Joshua and Caleb
Numbers 13, 14

I can choose right even when others choose wrong.

Joshua Obeys God
Deuteronomy 31, 34; Joshua 1

I can choose right even if I am afraid.

Joshua at Jericho
Joshua 5, 6

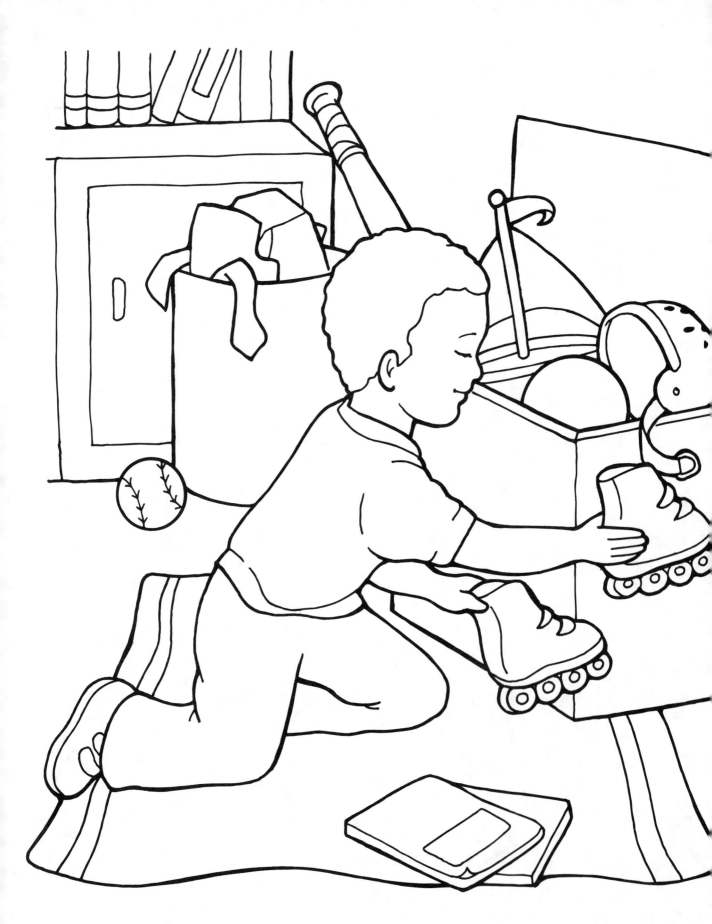

I can do what's right even when I don't understand.

God's People Do Right

Joshua 24

I can do right by obeying God's laws.

Deborah Helps Barak

Judges 4

I can help my friends do what's right.

Gideon Is Brave
Judges 6, 7

When I obey God, I am doing what's right.

Ruth Works Hard
Ruth 1, 2

When I work hard, I am doing what's right.

Hannah Keeps a Promise
1 Samuel 1

I can do right by keeping my promises.

Samuel Does Right
1 Samuel 2-4, 7

I want to follow God.

Samuel Anoints Saul

1 Samuel 8-10

I will try to obey God even when I don't want to.

Saul Disobeys God
1 Samuel 15

Choosing wrong makes God sad.

God Chooses David
1 Samuel 16

I will try to do what's right even when I am afraid.

David Cares for His Sheep
1 Samuel 16, 17

God helps me do my jobs.

David and Goliath
1 Samuel 17

God helps me be brave.

David and Jonathan
1 Samuel 18-20

Thank you, God, for my friends.

David Spares Saul's Life
1 Samuel 26

God helps me be kind.

Solomon Asks for Wisdom
1 Kings 3, 4

God hears my prayers.

Elijah Is Fed by Ravens
1 Kings 17

God gives me food.

Elijah and the Widow
1 Kings 17

Only God knows everything we need.

Elijah and the Prophets of Baal
1 Kings 18

God, you are powerful.

Micaiah Tells the Truth
1 Kings 22

I can do what's right. I can tell the truth.

God Heals Naaman
2 Kings 5

Only God can heal people.

The Shunammite Woman's Son
2 Kings 4

God controls everything.

Hezekiah Is Healed
2 Kings 20

God hears my prayer when I am sick.

Josiah and the Law
2 Kings 22, 23

I want to hear and obey God's laws.

Jehoshaphat Prays
2 Chronicles 20

God hears my prayer when I am afraid.

Manasseh Prays for Forgiveness
2 Chronicles 33

God hears my prayer when I am sorry.

Queen Esther Helps
Esther 1-5, 8

I want to do what's right even when it is hard.

Ezra and Nehemiah
Nehemiah 2-8

I want to do what's right.

Job Does Right
Job 1, 2, 42

God will help me do what's right.

Daniel and His Friends
Daniel 1

I will take care of my body.

The Fiery Furnace
Daniel 3

I will worship God and put him first.

Daniel Prays to God
Daniel 6

I will pray to God every day.

Jonah Changes His Mind
Jonah 1, 3

I can do right by obeying God.

Zechariah and Elizabeth
Luke 1

Let's celebrate!

An Angel Visits Mary
Luke 1

Let's sing about Jesus' birth!

Jesus Is Born
Luke 2

Thank you, God, for Jesus.

Shepherds and Angels

Luke 2

We celebrate Jesus' birth at Christmas.

Wise Men Worship Jesus
Matthew 2

I want to honor Jesus.

Simeon and Anna Thank God

Luke 2

Thank you, God, for Jesus.

Jesus Obeys His Parents
Luke 2

I can obey my parents.

John Baptizes Jesus
Matthew 3, Luke 2, John 1

I want to follow Jesus. He is God's Son.

Satan Tempts Jesus
Matthew 4

I will follow Jesus when I am tempted to do wrong.

Jesus' First Followers
John 1

I will follow Jesus, God's Son.

Jesus and Nicodemus
John 3

I can be a friend to a leader.

Jesus and the Samaritan Woman
John 4

I can be a friend to someone no one likes.

Jesus Heals a Sick Boy
John 4

Jesus has power to heal people.

Jesus Chooses Four Followers
Mark 1, Luke 5

I can tell my friends about Jesus.

Jesus Heals a Paralyzed Man
Mark 2

I can be a friend to someone who is sick.

Jesus Heals a Man at a Pool
John 5

Jesus can do things no one else can do.

Jesus Heals a Man's Hand
Mark 3

Jesus can heal anything.

Jesus Heals a Soldier's Servant
Luke 7

Jesus is special. He can do miracles.

Jesus Raises a Young Man to Life
Luke 7

Let's praise Jesus!

Jesus Forgives a Woman
Luke 7

I can be a friend to someone who is sorry for doing wrong

Jesus Stops a Storm
Mark 4

Jesus is powerful. He can change the weather!

Jairus's Daughter
Mark 5

Jesus can bring the dead to life.

Jesus Feeds 5,000
John 6

Jesus can feed a crowd with a little food.

Jesus Walks on Water
John 6

Jesus is more powerful than anything!

Jesus Heals a Deaf Man
Mark 7

Jesus is special. He can make the deaf hear.

The Mount of Transfiguration
Matthew 17

I will follow Jesus, our leader.

Jesus Heals a Blind Man
John 9

Jesus can make blind eyes see.

The Good Samaritan
Luke 10

I can follow Jesus by helping others.

The Lord's Prayer
Matthew 6, Luke 11

I can follow Jesus by praying to God.

The Greedy Farmer

Luke 12

I can follow Jesus by sharing.

Jesus Raises Lazarus
Luke 10, John 11

I can be a friend to someone who is sad.

The Ten Lepers
Luke 17

I can follow Jesus by being thankful.

Jesus and the Children
Mark 10

I can be a friend by being kind.

Jesus and Zaccheus
Luke 19

I can be a friend to someone who needs a friend.

The Triumphal Entry
John 12

I want to sing praise to Jesus.

The Last Supper
Luke 22

In Remembrance of Me

Jesus wants followers to remember him in a special way.

Jesus Is Alive
Matthew 27, 28, John 18-20

"Jesus has power over everything!"

Jesus Helps Catch Fish
John 21

"I know Jesus is alive."

Jesus' Church Begins
Acts 2

The church tells everyone Jesus' Good News.

Peter Heals a Lame Man
Acts 3, 4

I can help sick people learn about Jesus.

The Church Prays

Acts 4

I will pray for people who need to learn about Jesus.

Philip and the Ethiopian
Acts 8

I can tell my friends about Jesus.

Paul Begins to Tell About Jesus
Acts 9, 22

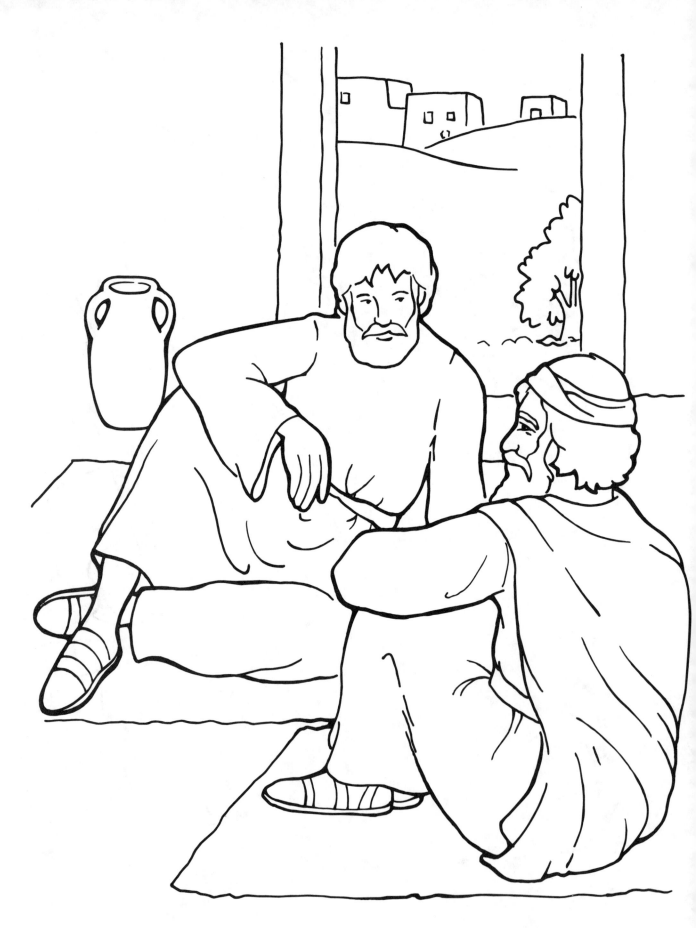

Paul learned that Jesus is God's Son.

Peter Raises Tabitha to Life
Acts 9

I can show my friends that Jesus loves them.

Paul Tells a Jailer About Jesus

Acts 16

I can tell others about Jesus even when it is hard.

Paul Tells a Crowd About Jesus
Acts 21, 22

I can tell others about Jesus no matter what.

Paul in Rome

Acts 28

Jesus loves everyone!

"In the beginning God created the sky and the earth."
Genesis 1:1

"Do what the Lord says is good and right.
Then things will go well for you." Deuteronomy 6:18

'ou must decide whom you will serve. . . . As for me and my
family, we will serve the Lord." Joshua 24:15

"I will praise you, Lord, with all my heart …
I will be happy because of you. God Most High,
I will sing praises to your name." Psalm 9:1, 2

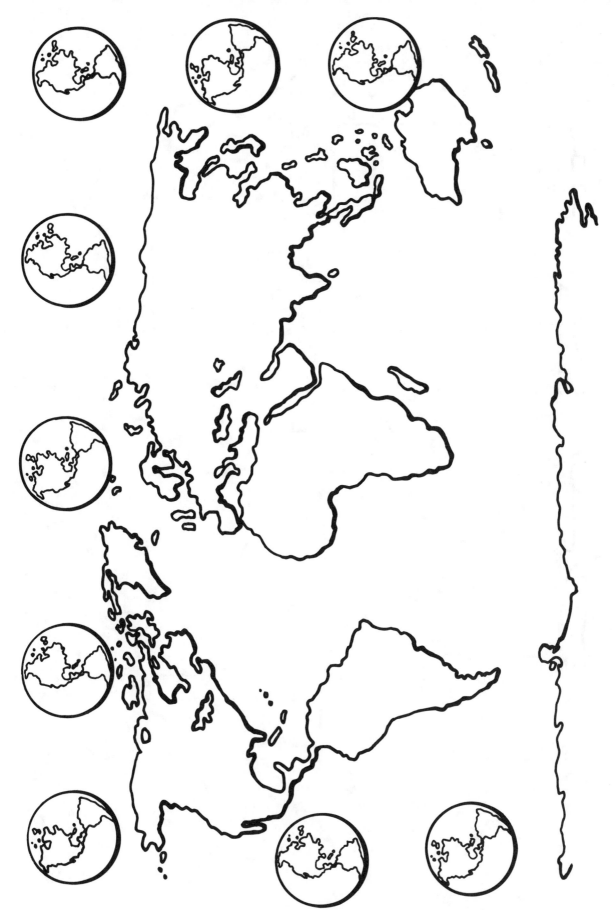

"Lord, all the nations you have made will come and worship you. Only you are God." Psalm 86:9, 10

"Give thanks to the Lord and pray to him. . . . Tell about all the wonderful things he has done." Psalm 105:1, 2

appy are those people who are fair, who do what is right at all times." Psalm 106:3

"Thank the Lord because he is good." Psalm 118:28, 29

"You are my God, and I will thank you. You are my God and I will praise your greatness. Thank the Lord because he is good. His love continues forever." Psalm 118:28, 29

"Lord, help me control my tongue.
Help me be careful about what I say." Psalm 141:3

"I will praise the Lord. Let everyone praise his holy name forever." Psalm 145:21

"Don't use your mouth to tell lies. . . . Keep your eyes focused on what is right." Proverbs 4:24, 25

"Honor God and obey his commands. This is the most important thing people can do. God knows everything people do, even the things done in secret." Ecclelsiastes 12:13, 14

"The Lord will do what he says."
Isaiah 38:7

"Jesus said to the followers, 'Go everywhere in the world. T
the Good News to everyone.'" Mark 16:15

he angel said to her, 'Don't be afraid, Mary, because God is
eased with you. . . . . You will give birth to a son, and you will
name him Jesus.'" Luke 1:30, 31

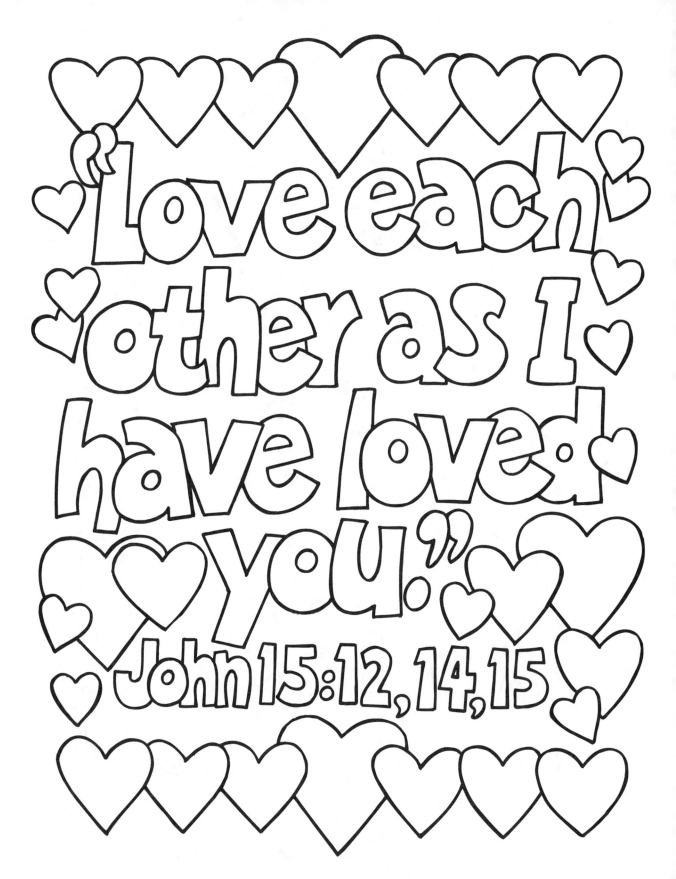

"This is my command: Love each other as I have loved you.
You are my friends if you do what I command you."
John 15:12, 14

"Jesus did many other miracles before his followers that are not written in this book." John 20:30

"We cannot keep quiet. We must speak about what we ha~
seen and heard." Acts 4:20

Christ . . . gave me the work of preaching the Good News."
1 Corinthians 1:17

"Follow the example of Christ." 1 Corinthians 11:1

"Children, obey your parents the way the Lord wants. This is the right thing to do." Ephesians 6:1

"Before we came to you, we suffered in Philippi. But our God
helped us to be brave and to tell you his Good News."
1 Thessalonians 2:2

sure that no one pays back wrong for wrong. But always try to do what is good for each other and for all people."
1 Thessalonians 5:15

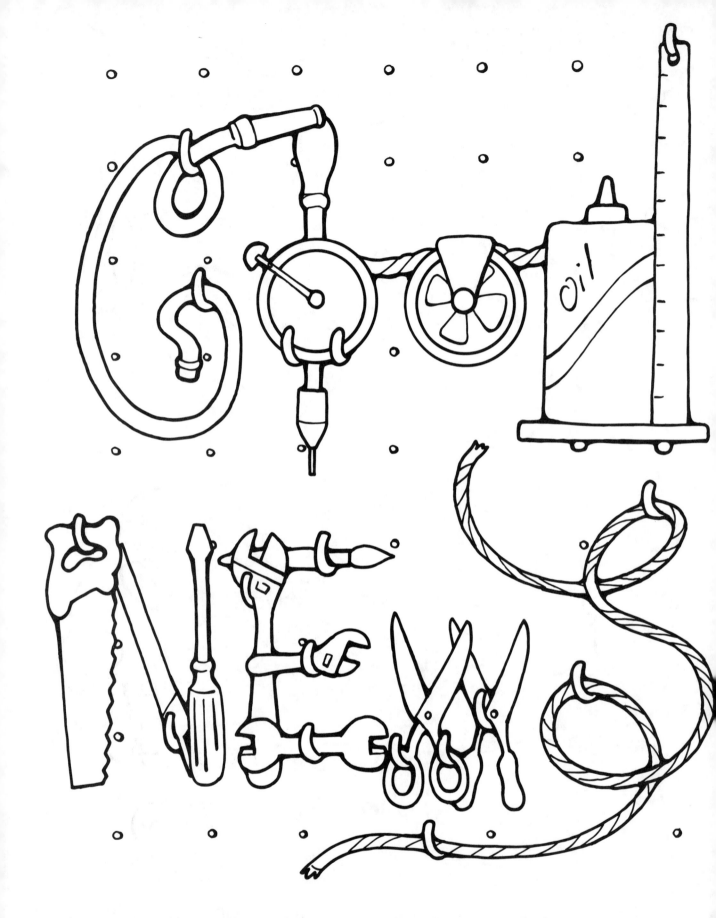

"Do the work of telling the Good News.
Do all the duties of a servant of God." 2 Timothy 4:5

"Christ . . . gave you an example to follow. So you should do as he did. He did no sin. He never lied." 1 Peter 2:21, 22

"Give all your worries to him, because he cares for you."
1 Peter 5:7

"I believe that Jesus is the Son of God." 1 John 4:15

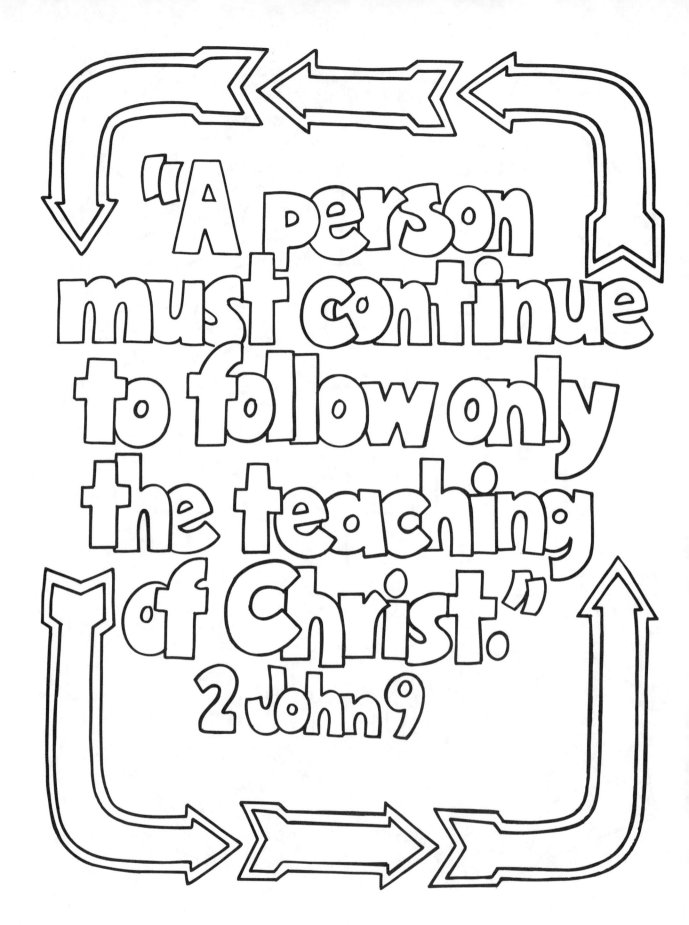

"A person must continue to follow only the teaching of Christ
2 John 9

INDEX

BIBLE STORIES
Old Testament
Abraham 21, 23
Creation 11, 13, 15, 17
Daniel 107, 111
David 69, 71, 73, 75, 77
Deborah 55
Elijah 81, 83, 85
Esther 101
Ezra 103
Gideon 57
Hannah 61
Hezekiah 93
Isaac 25, 29
Jacob 31
Jehoshaphat 97
Job 105
Jonah 113
Joseph 33, 35
Joshua 47, 49, 51, 53
Josiah 95
Manasseh 99
Micaiah 87
Moses and the Exodus 37, 39,
    41, 43, 45
Naaman 89
Nehemiah 103
Noah 17, 19
Rebekah 27
Ruth 59
Samuel 63, 65
Shadrach, Meshach, Abednego
    109
Shunammite Woman 91
Solomon 79
Saul 67

New Testament
Jesus' birth 117, 119, 121, 123
Jesus' early ministry 129, 131,
    133, 141
Jesus' growing up 127
Jesus' last week 183, 185, 187,
    189

Jesus' miracles 139, 143, 145,
    147, 149, 151, 155, 157,
    159, 161, 163, 165, 167, 175
Jesus' teaching 135, 137, 153,
    169, 171, 173, 177, 179, 181
Peter 191, 193, 195, 201
Philip 197
Paul 199, 203, 205, 207
Zechariah and Elizabeth 115

BIBLE THEMES
Worship God: He Made
    Everything 11, 12, 13, 14,
    15, 16
Worship God: He Keeps His
    Promises 17, 18, 19, 20, 21,
    22, 23, 24, 25, 26
Worship God: He Cares 37, 38,
    39, 40, 41, 42, 43, 44, 45, 46
Worship God: He Helps People
    71, 72, 73, 74, 75, 76, 77, 78
Worship God: He Is Powerful
    81, 82, 83, 84, 85, 86, 89,
    90
Worship God: He Hears
    Prayers: 79, 80, 93, 94, 97,
    98, 99, 100
Follow Jesus: Celebrate Jesus'
    Birth 115, 116, 117, 118,
    121, 122, 123, 124, 125, 126
Follow Jesus: Jesus Is the Son
    of God 117, 118, 119, 120,
    121, 122, 123, 124, 127,
    128, 129, 120, 131, 132,
    133, 134, 165, 166
Follow Jesus: Jesus Is Our
    Teacher 169, 170, 171, 172,
    173, 174, 177, 180
Follow Jesus: He Is a Friend
    133, 134, 135, 136, 137,
    138, 143, 144, 153, 154,
    175, 176, 179, 180, 181, 182

Tell About Jesus: Jesus Is
    Special 139, 140, 145, 146,
    159, 160, 161, 162
Tell About Jesus: Jesus Is Alive
    151, 152, 183, 184, 187,
    188, 189, 190, 191, 192
Tell About Jesus: Jesus' Special
    Church 193, 194, 195, 196,
    197, 198, 201, 202
Tell About Jesus: Learn About
    Jesus 148, 149, 155, 156,
    157, 158, 163, 164, 167, 168
Tell About Jesus: Tell Others
    About Jesus 149, 150, 185,
    186, 187, 188, 199, 200
Tell About Jesus: Tell About
    Jesus When It Is Difficult
    203, 204, 205, 206, 207, 208
Do Right: Do Right Wherever
    You Are 23, 24, 27, 28, 29,
    30, 33, 34, 35, 36
Do Right: Do What Is Right
    47, 48, 49, 50, 515, 52, 53,
    54, 87, 88, 95, 96, 101, 102,
    103, 104
Do Right: Do Right at Home
    and School 105, 106, 107,
    108, 109, 110, 111, 112
Do Right: Do Right When It is
    Hard 55, 56, 57, 58, 59, 60,
    61, 62, 113, 114
Do Right: Do What God Says
    Is Right 63, 64, 65, 66, 67,
    68, 69, 70

BIBLE VERSES
Do Right 210, 211, 215. 217.
    219, 220, 229
Follow Jesus 223, 224, 228,
    231, 233, 235, 236,
Tell About Jesus 222, 225, 226,
    227, 230, 232
Worship God 209, 212, 213,
    214, 216, 218, 221, 234

CORRELATION TO STANDARD'S
4ˢ & 5ˢ / PRIMARY CURRICULUM

The lesson titles for Standard Publishing's 4's & 5's/Primary Sunday school curriculum are listed below. Th
are grouped by quarters and listed in the order they appear in the teacher's books. In parentheses are th
numbers for the coloring pages that correlate to that lesson.

FALL, YEAR ONE
God Makes the World (11, 12)
God Makes the Animals (13, 14)
God Makes People (15, 16)
God Saves Noah (17, 18)
God Gives a Sign (19, 20)
Abraham's New Home (21, 22)
The Birth of Isaac (25, 26)
God Cares for Jacob (31, 32)
God Cares for Baby Moses (37, 38)
God Cares for His People (39, 40)
God's People at the Red Sea (41, 42)
God Gives Food and Water (43, 44)
God Gives Rules (45, 46)

WINTER, YEAR ONE
An Angel Visits Mary (117, 118)
Jesus is Born (119, 120)
Shepherds Tell Others (121, 122)
Wise Men Worship Jesus (123, 124)
Jesus Obeys His Parents (127, 128)
Jesus Chooses Four Friends (141, 142)
Jesus and the Children (179, 180)
Jesus and Nicodemus (135, 136)
Jesus Is a Friend ((175, 176)
Jesus and the Samaritan Woman (137, 138)
Jesus and Zacchaeus (181, 182)
Jesus Forgives a Woman (153, 154)
Jesus and the Paralyzed Man (143, 144)

SPRING, YEAR ONE
Jesus Stops a Storm (155, 156)
The Man Who Can't Hear (163, 164)
The Man Who Can't See (167, 168)
Jesus Heals a Man's Hand (147, 148)
Jairus' Daughter (157, 158)
The Soldier's Servant (149, 150)
The Last Supper (185, 186)
Jesus Is Alive (187, 188)
Paul Tells About Jesus (199, 200)
Paul Tells a Jailer (203, 204)
Paul Tells a Crowd (205, 206)
Paul Tells Islanders (204, 206, 208)
Paul in Rome (207, 208)

SUMMER, YEAR ONE
Joshua and Caleb (47, 48)
Joshua Obeys God (49, 50)
Joshua at Jericho (51, 52)
God's People Do Right (53, 54)
Deborah Helps Barak (55, 56)
Gideon is Brave (57, 58)
Ruth Works Hard (59, 60)
Jonah Changes His Mind (113, 114)
Hannah Keeps a Promise (61, 62)
Samuel Does Right (63, 64)
Samuel Obeys God (65, 66)
Saul Disobeys God (67, 68)
God Chooses David (69, 70)

FALL, YEAR TWO

David Does His Job (71, 72)
David Is Brave (73, 74)
David and Jonathan (75, 76)
David Is Kind (77, 78)
God Sends Ravens (81, 82)
God Provides Bread (83, 84)
God Sends Fire (85, 86)
God Heals Naaman (89, 90)
God Makes a Boy Live Again (91, 92)
God Hears Solomon (79, 80)
God Hears Hezekiah (93, 94)
God Hears Manasseh (99, 100)
God Hears Jehoshaphat (97, 98)

WINTER, YEAR TWO

Elizabeth and Zechariah (115, 116)
Mary Sings (117, 118)
Shepherds Tell About Jesus (121, 122)
Simeon and Anna Thank God (125, 126)
Wise Men Visit Jesus (123, 124)
John Baptizes Jesus (129, 130)
Satan Tempts Jesus (131, 132)
Jesus' First Followers (133, 134)
God Calls Jesus His Son (165, 166)
The Model Prayer (171, 172)
The Greedy Farmer (173, 174)
The Good Samaritan (169, 170)
The Ten Lepers (177, 178)

SPRING, YEAR TWO

Jesus Heals a Sick Boy (139, 140)
The Man at the Pool (145, 146)
Jesus Feeds 5,000 (159, 160)
Jesus Walks on Water (161, 162)
A Young Man Lives Again (151, 152)
People Praise Jesus (183, 184)
Jesus' Resurrection (187, 188)
Jesus Helps Catch Fish (189, 190)
Jesus' Church Begins (191, 192)
The Church Helps (193, 194)
The Church Prays (195, 196)
The Church Tells (197, 198)
The Church Loves (201, 202)

SUMMER, YEAR TWO

Abraham and Lot (23, 24)
Rebekah Shows Kindness (27, 38)
Isaac Is a Peacemaker (29, 30)
Joseph's Best Work (33, 34)
Joseph Forgives His Brothers (35, 36)
Micaiah Tells the Truth (87, 88)
King Josiah and the Law (95, 96)
Queen Esther Helps (101, 102)
Ezra and Nehemiah Do Right (103, 104)
Job Does Right (105, 106)
Daniel and His Friends (107, 108)
Daniel's Friends Do Right (109, 110)
Daniel Prays to God (111, 112)